activities

for
anyone,
anytime,
anywhere

Children's Museum Activity Books

Bubbles
Ball-Point Pens
Milk Carton Blocks
Messing Around with Baking Chemistry
Messing Around with Water Pumps and Siphons
Messing Around with Drinking Straw Construction
Activities for Anyone, Anytime, Anywhere

activities
for anyone, anytime, anywhere

A CHILDREN'S MUSEUM ACTIVITY BOOK

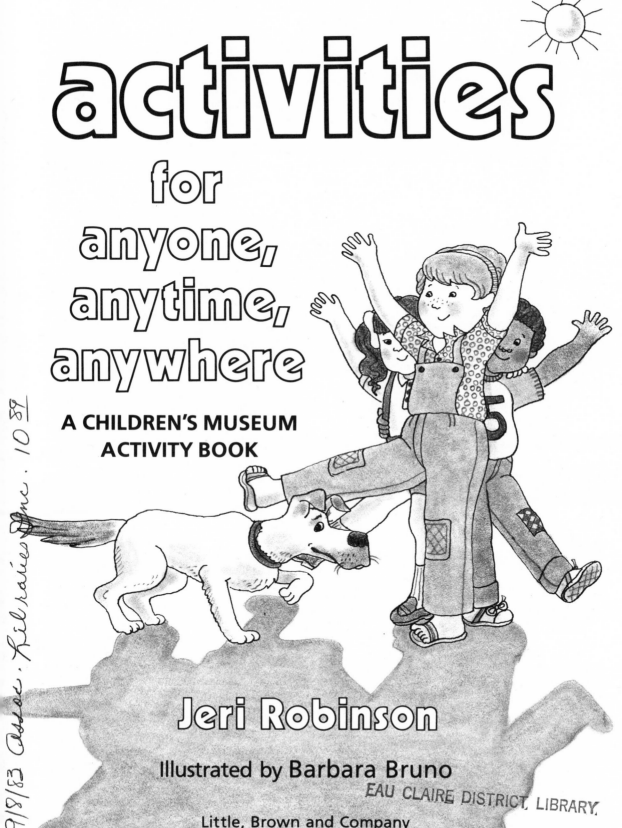

Jeri Robinson

Illustrated by Barbara Bruno

Little, Brown and Company
Boston   Toronto

Library of Congress Cataloging in Publication Data
Robinson, Jeri.
  Activities for anyone, anytime, anywhere.
  1. Amusements. 2. Games. I. Title.
GV1201.R56   790.1   80-15353
ISBN 0-316-75144-8   AACR2
ISBN 0-316-75145-6 (pbk.)

Designed by S. M. Sherman

VB
Published simultaneously in Canada
by Little, Brown & Company (Canada) Limited

PRINTED IN THE UNITED STATES OF AMERICA

Contents

For
Leon and Fannie Robinson

With special thanks to Dorothy Merrill and Liz Hastie, with whom
I presented many of these ideas in workshops, and all of the
parents and children who visited Grownups and Kids and Playspace
to learn how to do them

Introduction

This is a book about the kinds of situation that parents, grandparents, teachers, baby-sitters, play group leaders, camp counselors, and others who care for children always wish they had planned for after it's already too late. It's about the forty-five minutes between the time dinner burns and the moment a substitute meal is ready. It's about outdoor birthday parties that get rained on, being stuck in bed with a cold, waiting an hour in the doctor's office, and taking impromptu field trips in your own backyard.

This book is an outgrowth of the exhibits and educational development work associated with the early childhood programs of the Boston Children's Museum. The materials and activities presented have been used with and by children in a variety of settings, including the museum's — Grownups and Kids, art and craft activity area, and Playspace, an environment where adults and older youngsters can observe the developmental abilities of children of different ages.

With children in the museum, as often happens at home, on the road, in a preschool classroom or an after-school program, the need occasionally arises to conduct an instant but nonetheless engaging activity to fill in for a plan gone somehow awry. All activities are low-cost, with most materials easily available in your kitchen, from throwaways (see the Tools of the Trade list), or from discount department stores. Some may be considered "quickies," taking only a few moments to prepare and present; others need some advance preparation and can be made to last for a few minutes, an hour, or the course of several days. Some will need adult supervision, but many others can be prepared and carried out by older children on their own.

In the Notes to Adults section, you'll find some ideas I have found helpful when working or traveling with groups of kids. Notes to Kids offers some suggestions for kids to keep in mind as they choose and plan their own activities.

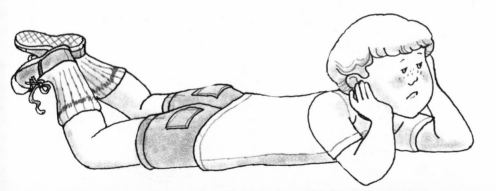

The activities are divided into six sections:

I. Getting Started
II. Quickies and Longies for Unexpected Moments
III. Celebrations
IV. Sick in Bed
V. On the Road
VI. Exploring the Great Out-of-Doors.

Keep in mind that all of these activities have been done successfully by people with no specialized arts and crafts training. I'm sure you'll develop a repertoire of ideas that will give you much pleasure.

Jeri Robinson
1982

Notes to Adults

As a parent, you may not think of yourself as a teacher or group leader. However, in the course of your child's growing-up years, you may find yourself acting as class parent, field trip chaperone, scout leader, or church school teacher. In any event, these hints for working and traveling with groups may prove helpful. Here are some points to ponder as you begin to plan your activities.

Working with Kids

How old? Preschoolers and school-age children have very different abilities and attention spans. In general, the younger the child, the easier the activity should be (with fewer materials and simpler directions).

How many? Group size also depends on the age of the kids and the complexity of the activity. Try to keep groups as small as possible — one leader or helper for each group of 5 preschoolers or 9 elementary-school-age kids. Again, the more complicated the activity, the smaller you want the group.

How well do you know them? If you are unsure of the abilities of kids in the group, choose a simple game or activity that will provide you with an opportunity to become acquainted with them and their abilities.

How well do they know each other? If the group is one that has known each other for a while (scout troop, Sunday school class, cousins from several families), you may expect the kids to work together reasonably well, sharing materials, etc. For groups just getting acquainted, or together for only a short time (for example, guests at a birthday party), provide a variety of activities that will help the children become more comfortable with each other.

What have they been doing and what will they be doing following this activity? It is important to be aware of where a particular activity fits into the rest of the schedule. For example, on a long bus trip, you might need to plan a rest stop that combines a period of active play with a more settling rest period — a snack, story time, or a relaxed group game — before reboarding.

Where are you? Bus station, church basement, highway rest area, your kitchen, on an airplane? Providing the proper setting increases the potential success of a given activity. Plan messy activities where there are water and adequate cleaning supplies nearby. Respect the rights of others; group singing may not be appreciated by all passengers on a crowded train.

What prepared activities do you have on hand? Many activities can be prepared ahead, boxed, and taken down and used when needed, such as play dough, simple printing, or collage work. These are particularly useful for spur-of-the-moment situations.

What materials are available or easily accessible? You may want to start an activity card file, listing those activities for which you usually have the materials on hand in good supply (such as newspapers or coat hangers) or have easy access to (shoeboxes, paper towel tubes).

How much help do you have or need? If the group is large and there are few adults, keep the activity simple. Play games, read stories or poems, allow the children to draw, etc., but keep it manageable.

How well do you know the activity? When at all possible, try out a new activity yourself before doing it with a large group. This will provide you with an opportunity to make any adjustments or work out solutions for any potential pitfalls.

Traveling with Groups

To the Playground

Many of my kindergartners' early "field trips" were to neighboring playgrounds. In addition to our general playground paraphernalia — balls, ropes, skates — we were never without our Park Trip Kit. Here's what it contained (because of the unpredictable conditions of many city parks and playgrounds, we took along several items you may find it unnecessary to pack).

Trip bag. Waterproof canvas drawstring book bag, which contained:
  large brown grocery bag
  kitchen-size plastic garbage bag
  pair of cloth garden gloves

Before allowing the children to run loose, we all made a quick survey of the area for broken glass, cans, paper trash, and other rubbish. Children placed cans and paper in the plastic bag, and the adults, wearing the garden gloves, picked up all glass and placed it in the paper bag. Both bags could then be disposed of at the park, if trashcans were available, or returned to school if they weren't.

Emergency number book. This notebook contained the names of all the children, their emergency contacts, and any pertinent medical information. Inside the cover were the phone numbers of the school, police, ambulance, and local clinic. There were also five dimes taped to the cover for emergency phone calls.

Wash-and-Dries. These were essential for cleaning sticky or dirty fingers and mouths, also for wiping sweaty foreheads.

Tissues. For drying tears and blowing runny noses.

First aid kit, or small can of Bactine, Band-Aids. For cuts, no matter how minuscule.

Lollipops. To soothe the victim.

Damp washcloth. This was carried in a Ziploc plastic bag and washed out daily, even if it hadn't been used. (A damp cloth is good for removing dirt and grime so that a wound can be seen.)

Snacks. On longer trips, we often took along a bag of apple or pear quarters, individual boxes of raisins, or celery and carrot sticks. For napkins, we cut the folded edges of commercial paper table napkins to get four out of one. The snacks also served as a way of calming down the group for the trek back to school.

Books. I always included two or three storybooks and a collection of poems. The books could be enjoyed by a single child or read to the whole group during the snack break. Reading poetry was one of our favorite ways of ending a trip to the park.

On Field Trips

Advance Information ("What to Know before You Go")

With the rising costs of bus rentals and fuel and admission fees, knowing in advance as much as possible about your destination can obviate many hassles and disappointments.

If possible, secure previsit information or, better still, visit the potential trip site. Many museums, national parks, and historic houses encourage teachers and group leaders to visit ahead and sometimes provide previsit orientations. The information you receive may suggest ways of preparing your group for the trip as well as give you ideas for other related activities. Share with the chaperones and children any information they should know in advance, such as special rules or restrictions. Children are often more attentive and enjoy trips more if they have been properly prepared.

Once you've started investigating potential trip sites, you might find it useful to start a field-trip file box. Make up a set of cards similar to the sample, and fill them in as needed. You will find it an invaluable resource for yourself as well as for other colleagues.

MUSEUMS

PARKS

CITY TRIPS

THE ZOO

Trip Card

CONTACT PERSON _____ HOURS _____

PHONE _____

NAME OF PLACE _____ ADULT-CHILD RATIO _____

ADDRESS _____ ADMISSION FEES _____

ACCESSIBILITY TO PUBLIC TRANSPORTATION _____ SPECIAL COSTS _____

RECOMMENDED AGE OF VISITORS _____

SUGGESTED LENGTH OF VISIT _____

GROUP RATES _____ RESTAURANT

PREVISIT INFORMATION OR ORIENTATION AVAILABLE _____ ___ SNACK BAR

___ INDOOR PICNIC

___ OUTDOOR PICNIC

FACILITIES (CHECK IF AVAILABLE) ___ TOUR GUIDES ___ ANY OF ABOVE NEARBY

___ BATHROOMS ___ BILINGUAL AIDES

___ PAY TELEPHONE ___ FREE/PAY COAT RM

___ FIRST AID ___ FREE/PAY CAR PKNG.

___ WHEELCHAIR ACCESSIBILITY ___ FREE/PAY BUS PKNG.

___ GIFT SHOP

PROGRAM DESCRIPTION _____

NEARBY SITES OF INTEREST TO CHILDREN _____

POSTVISIT COMMENTS (dated) _____

Transportation

Car pools. In addition to the driver, there should be at least one other adult in each car. Everyone should follow the safety procedures of using a seat belt, and no standing, changing seats, or roughhousing, in addition to any other rules the driver of the car has (e.g., no eating, yelling).

Chartered bus. Have adults sit among the children at well-spaced intervals throughout the bus and, just as for riding in cars, make sure children and adults know and agree to all rules before boarding. Have an organized procedure for getting on and off the bus (I've found filling the bus from back to front is easiest). If necessary, assign sections of the bus or certain seats to particular groups. If eating is allowed, be sure there are trash bags available.

Public transportation. The most welcome group on a bus or train is a well-mannered and orderly one. As when walking, remind your charges to be considerate of others. When a group is taking public transportation, the role of the chaperone is extremely important. Each chaperone should handle the carfare for his/her group, make sure the group stays together on the bus, and be aware of the route and final destination if the subgroup somehow becomes separated from the others.

Money

Whenever possible, collect money in advance for transportation and admissions.

If children have extra spending money, provide each child with a small envelope in which to put his or her own. Have the child write his or her name and the amount on the envelope, seal it, and return it to you.

With groups of younger children I have often added an extra 50 or 75 cents to the cost of the trip and asked that no additional money be brought along. Doing this will assure that all children may choose snacks or souvenirs of similar value.

Food

Lunches. Try to leave lunchboxes behind and pack lunches in well-marked brown bags. In hot weather, remind parents not to pack sandwich meats, or salads or sandwiches made with mayonnaise, or anything else that will spoil if unrefrigerated.

To avoid having lunches lost or eaten early, consider collecting the group's lunches and carrying them in a plastic shopping bag or a Styrofoam cooler. Be sure to bring along extra napkins, trash bags, and Wash-and-Dries for cleanup.

Snacks. At ball games, circuses, ice shows, and the like, the concessions can be more outstanding than the entertainment. Not only are they expensive, however, but you can find yourself spending half the show hailing the popcorn man and passing out Cokes.

Before your next trip, collect 50 cents from each child (or solicit donations from parents) and make your own snack packs. You might want to consider including a choice of fresh fruit wedges or carrot and celery sticks and small cans of juice. Each child might choose two or three of the small bags.

A good snack for spectators and sports enthusiasts alike is GORP (Good Old Raisins and Peanuts). You can simply combine equal amounts of raisins and peanuts or add some combination of the following:

Notes to Kids

This book has lots of activities you can do on your own or with friends or younger sisters and brothers. Before you begin, you may want to look through the book several times and choose some activities you might want to try at a later time.

When you are ready to get started:

1. Read the activity instructions and make sure you have all the necessary equipment. If there is anything you don't understand, or that you need help with, ask an adult.

2. Make sure you have a good uncluttered work space (such as a floor or table top) and be sure to cover it with newspaper or an old plastic tablecloth before doing anything messy.

3. Protect yourself! Change into your old clothes before painting, or make yourself a coverall (see Getting Started section).

4. Clean up and put everything away until your next activity time.

You might need to try a new activity several times before you get the knack of it, so don't be discouraged if something doesn't come out the first time exactly as you expected.

I. Getting Started

Tools of the Trade

Many of the items on the list below are household recyclables or can be salvaged from your trash. Others may be purchased at a local department store, a stationery store, or supermarket, or 5 and 10.

baby-food jars

bags

beads

berry baskets

bottles

brushes

buttons

cans (soup, juice, coffee, or
    tuna; make sure the edges
    are smooth)

cardboard

cellophane

chalk

chopsticks

clay

clothespins

coat hangers

construction paper

contact paper (clear)

cookie cutters

cookie sheets

cottage-cheese cartons

crayons

crepe paper

dowels

egg cartons

eggshells

envelopes

fabric scraps

felt

finger paints

foil

food coloring

glue (white all-purpose)

greeting cards (used)

hammer

handkerchiefs

iron

keys (old)

magazines
magnets
magnifying glass
markers (felt-tipped)

nails
needles
newspaper
newsprint

oil crayons

paper (of all kinds)
paper bags
paper clips
paper cups
paper cutter
paper plates
paper punch
paper towels
paper towel tubes
paste
pencils
pens
plaster of paris
plastic bags (sandwich, storage,
   garbage)
plastic silverware
popsicle sticks
poster board

Q-Tips

rags
ribbons

rubber bands
rulers

scissors
shelf paper
socks (old)
sponges
spools
staplers
staples
straws
string

telephone wire
thread
tissue paper
tissues
toilet paper rollers
tongue depressors
toothbrushes (old)
toothpicks
tracing paper
typing paper

wallpaper
wax paper
wood scraps
wrapping paper

yarn
yogurt containers

Ziploc bags

Stock Supplies
Useful Recipes for Arts and Crafts Materials

These recipes can be made ahead and stored until needed.

Play Dough (not for eating)

You'll need:
  2 cups flour
  1 cup salt
  ¾ cup water
  few drops food coloring
  2 tablespoons cooking oil

What to do:
In a large bowl, mix together the flour and salt. Add the food coloring and oil to the water. Slowly add the water mixture to the flour mixture, kneading until a soft dough is formed.

Store in a plastic bag or covered container and refrigerate when not using. It will last about 2 weeks.

Projects made from this dough can be air-dried or dried in a 250° oven for 1½ to 2 hours, then painted with poster or acrylic paints.

Peanut Butter Play Dough (that you can eat!)

You'll need:

2 cups powdered dry milk
2 cups smooth peanut butter
1 cup honey

What to do:

Mix all the ingredients together. The result will be a soft, pliable, good-tasting modeling dough. It is especially good for younger children, who are often tempted to eat conventional play dough.

Bubble Solution

You'll need:

1 quart warm water
¼ cup liquid dishwashing detergent (Joy and Dawn work best)
a ½-gallon plastic jug or jar with a lid

What to do:

Pour the water into the plastic jar. Add the detergent and stir gently. This solution can be saved for weeks and used as needed for blowing bubbles. Straws, funnels, spools, and berry baskets make good quick bubble-blowers. For a super-bubble straw, cut both ends off 3 or 4 soup cans (make sure the edges are smooth), stack them on top of each other, and join them with masking tape. You can blow a giant bubble with this!

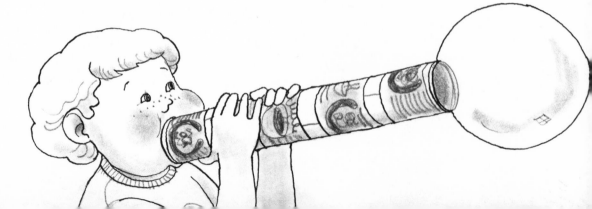

Mock Food Color

You'll need:
    several yards of crepe paper streamers, in 3 or 4 colors
    lukewarm water
    paper cups
    jelly jars with lids

What to do:
Rip crepe paper into small pieces. Place pieces by color in separate paper cups, then cover with water. Let stand a few minutes. Squeeze the dye from the crepe paper, then discard the wet paper and store the dyed water in jelly jars.

To make very dark dye, use twice as much paper or half as much water. This is a good dye for coloring paper towels. It can also be used in making play dough.

A weaker dye solution can be used for "water color" painting, using Q-Tips for brushes.

NOTE: The dyes used in making crepe paper are nontoxic; however, treat them with the same precautionary measures you would use with any other dye solution. This "dye" washes out of most fabrics, but smocks should be worn to protect clothing.

Paste

You'll need:

- 2-quart saucepan
- 1 cup flour
- 1 cup sugar
- 1 cup cold water
- 4 cups boiling water (Let an adult handle this!)
- a few drops of oil of wintergreen (available at a drugstore)
- 2-quart jar

What to do:

Mix flour and sugar. Slowly stir in cold water. Slowly add boiling water, stirring vigorously to prevent lumps. Bring mixture to a boil, stirring constantly; cook until thick and clear. Add oil of wintergreen. When it cools, store in a covered jar. Makes 1½ quarts.

Colored Glue

You'll need:
  white glue
  concentrated food coloring or powdered paint
  paper cups
  clean squeeze bottles from honey or home permanents

What to do:
Pour white glue into paper cups. Add a different color to each until the desired tone is produced. Pour into the squeeze bottles. This is great for collage work and sand paintings.

Hunk of Crayon

You'll need:
  broken bits of crayon sorted by color
  soup cans or coffee cans
  saucepan partly full of hot water
  foil muffin-tin liners

What to do:
Scrape off any dirt or bit of paper from the crayon pieces before sorting. Place the crayon bits in cans, one color to a can. Set the cans in the pan of hot water. (If you start with the lightest colors first, then the next-lightest, etc., you can use the same can over and over.) When the melted wax has slightly cooled, pour it into the foil liners. When the crayon has hardened, it should pop out easily.

You can make a multicolored crayon by pouring equal amounts of several colors into a liner and swirling it slightly.

Coveralls

Waterproof smocks can be made in a matter of minutes from plastic trash bags, drop cloths, or sheeting. Here's how.

Trash Bag Coverall

You'll need:
  garbage bags (tall kitchen size for little kids, lawn or leaf bags for
    older kids)
  scissors

What to do:
With the closed end at the top, fold the bag in half lengthwise (A) and cut through all thicknesses, as shown in B.

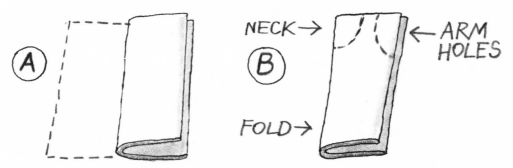

If necessary, enlarge the neck opening by cutting on the dotted line, as shown (do one side only).

For a sash, cut a one-inch strip off the bottom of the bag and tie it around the waist. If the smock is too long, cut it to an appropriate length.

SASH

Plastic Sheeting Smock

You'll need:
   plastic sheeting (the kind sold for drop cloths or storm windows)
   measuring tape or yardstick
   scissors

What to do:
Measure the person from the knees up over the shoulders to the middle of the back.

Cut a piece of the sheeting to this length; make it 18 to 24 inches wide.

Fold it at the shoulder line and cut a hole for only the head, as shown.

On the front, cut up 1½ inches from the edge on each side, stopping 2 inches above the waist.

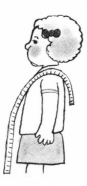 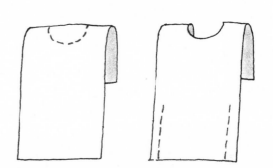

Pull the smock over the person's head, with the short side behind.

Tie it in the back.

II. Quickies and Longies for Unexpected Moments

Quickies

Burned dinners, flat tires, and rain showers are never planned for, but they occur and can spoil even the best-laid plans. Here are some "quickies" that use things you're bound to have on hand. With a minimum of preparation, you can change a potentially disappointing afternoon into a fun one.

Simple Symphonies

Here are two "musical instruments" that can be enjoyed by the musician and for which no one has to be an unwilling audience.

Bonger

You'll need:
   a wire coat hanger
   a string

What to do:
Cut a piece of string as long as your arm. Tie one end to one side of the straight bottom of the hanger, the other end to the other side. Hang the string over the top of your head, holding one side near each ear. Then swing the hook end of the hanger so that it hits against a table or some other surface, and listen to your secret symphony.

Earharp

You'll need:

a bottle cap (The kind that you need a bottle-opener to remove is best.)

a small, skinny rubber band

What to do:

Wrap the rubber band 2 or 3 times around the bottle cap, carefully, forming 2 or 3 strings. Hold the cap near your ear and pluck the strings gently.

Puzzles

Box Front Jigsaw

You'll need:

box fronts from detergent, cereal, cracker, and cookie boxes

scissors

envelopes or plastic bags for storage

What to do:

Cut the box fronts up into as many or as few pieces as you like. For a more challenging puzzle, cut all pieces into like shapes, such as squares, rectangles, or triangles.

Strip Puzzles

You'll need:
- magazine pictures
- cardboard
- rubber cement
- scissors
- marking pen

What to do:

Find colored magazine pictures or advertisements that can be described by a single word (for example, tree, flower, girl, truck, car, boat).

Cut a piece of cardboard the width of the picture and at least one inch longer.

Mount the picture on the cardboard, using rubber cement, leaving the extra inch margin at the base.

Write the one-word description of the picture evenly spaced across the base. Cut the picture into strips with a separate letter on each strip.

Mix up the strips, then put them back together in the right order (check the spelling; it will help).

Freaky Pictures

You'll need:
   magazines
   scissors
   glue

What to do:
Choose a fairly good-sized picture with a lot of action and small detail (for example, a scene of a dinner party, a group on a ski slope).

Find pictures in other magazines and cut out things that would change the character of the original picture (for example, an animal head to go on the body of a ballet dancer, a pair of boots to go on a dinner table; the possibilities are limitless).

Half-a-Face

You'll need:
   magazines
   large sheets of paper
   scissors
   glue
   crayons

What to do:
Find large full-face pictures in magazines and cut them out.

Cut each picture in half and mount it on a larger sheet of paper, making sure that there is room to draw in the other half of the picture.

Now use your imagination!

27

Play Dough (See pages 17 and 18 for recipes.)

Play dough, clay dough, or play clay is a good standby, and it can be used and enjoyed by kids of all ages. Here are a few variations for added pleasure.

- Add a few drops of your favorite flavorings or spice for a pleasant-smelling dough.
- Use rubber-stamp letters to imprint messages on play dough pendants before they harden.
- Use a straw to make a hole in clay pendants for hanging them.
- Peanut butter play dough is both nutritious and a good modeling medium for younger children. (See recipe, page 18.)

Fancy Names

You'll need:
    paper
    pens, pencils, or crayons

What to do:
Use your name as the basis for a design. Find a fancy way to sign it or make a jazzy design with your initials.

3-D Initials

You'll need:
    lightweight cardboard or manila file folders
    tissue paper cut into 2-inch squares
    pencil
    scissors
    glue

What to do:
Draw a large initial on the cardboard. Cut it out.

Spread a thin layer of glue on a small section of the cutout and cover it with tissue-paper puffs. Continue until the entire letter is covered.

To make a puff:

Place your finger in the center of a square of tissue paper and pull the sides of the paper up around your finger. Press the puff firmly onto the cardboard and remove your finger. The tissue will stick to the cardboard.

This technique can be used for all kinds of decorations.

Blot Pictures

You'll need:

   paintbrush (the kind that comes in a watercolor set, number 7 or 7¼)
   small containers of poster paint (2 or 3 colors)
   paper

What to do:

Fold a piece of paper in half and open it again.

Drop a few blobs of paint on one side of the paper.

Refold the paper like a book and rub it lightly with your hand, then open it.

You can cover these pictures with clear contact paper and use them to cover small books, or you can trace and cut out a butterfly shape and use the butterflies for window or wall decorations.

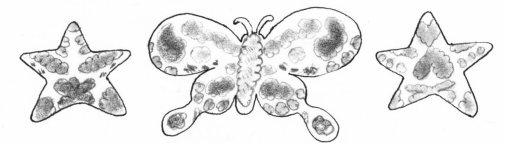

Straw Painting

You'll need:
    small containers of poster paint
    drinking straws
    construction paper

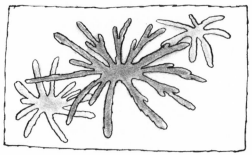

What to do:
Place a blob or two of paint on the construction paper.

Holding a straw close to the paint, blow gently through it until the paint forms a design.

NOTE: Always be sure to cover your work space or table with newspaper or an old plastic tablecloth before painting!

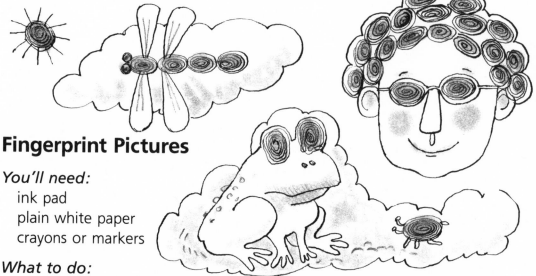

Fingerprint Pictures

You'll need:
    ink pad
    plain white paper
    crayons or markers

What to do:
Experiment making interesting finger- and thumbprints with an old ink pad. Turn them into interesting creatures by drawing on wings, feet, and faces.

Put these prints on the upper left-hand corner of blank white paper and use the paper as your personal stationery. You might want to decorate some envelopes to match.

Suggestion: Use washable or non-waterproof ink on a new ink pad. Or give a warning that it will not wash out of clothes, though it will come off bodies.

Instant Minibook

With a few simple folds and a single cut or tear, you can turn a single sheet of paper into an 8-page booklet. If you turn it inside out, you can make a 16-page book.

You'll need:
 a rectangular sheet of paper
 a pair of scissors

What to do:
Take a rectangular sheet of paper and fold it in half lengthwise.

Open it, then fold it in half crosswise.

Fold it crosswise again.

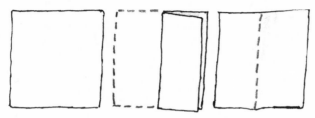

Unfold it so that the paper is back as in step 2. Cut a slit halfway up the middle, like this:

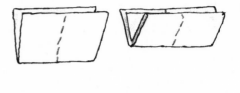

Open the paper and fold it lengthwise again as in step 1, with the slit on the top.

Grasp it at either end and push the ends of the slit together like this:

Fold it at one edge, like this, to make a book:

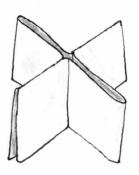

Punch two holes along the folded edge. Tie string or yarn through the holes to bind the book's pages together.

Longies

Ever have a rain shower turn into a full-fledged storm, or been cooped up for several days during a blizzard? Here are some longer activities that you can start and stop, or add on to, as time and interest permit.

Impromptu Dollhouse

You'll need:
  glue
  scissors
  4 shoeboxes
  spools, large and small
  toothpaste caps or bottle caps
  scraps of fabric
  odds and ends of gift-wrap
  large stamps
  small pictures from magazines
  smaller boxes

What to do:
A dollhouse improvised on the spur of the moment can be more fun than any other kind.

Stack the shoeboxes any way you want, just making sure that they are all open on the same side.

Make furniture out of the things listed above, or other items found around the house.

Tables are circles or squares of cloth pasted onto large thread spools.

Stools and chairs are smaller spools.

Lampshades or vases are toothpaste caps or other caps.

Sheets and blankets are scraps of fabric.

Odds and ends of gift-wrap paper can be wallpaper.

Wool fabric scraps can be rugs.

The stamps or small cutouts from magazines are pictures for the walls.

Beds and sofas can be made from smaller boxes.

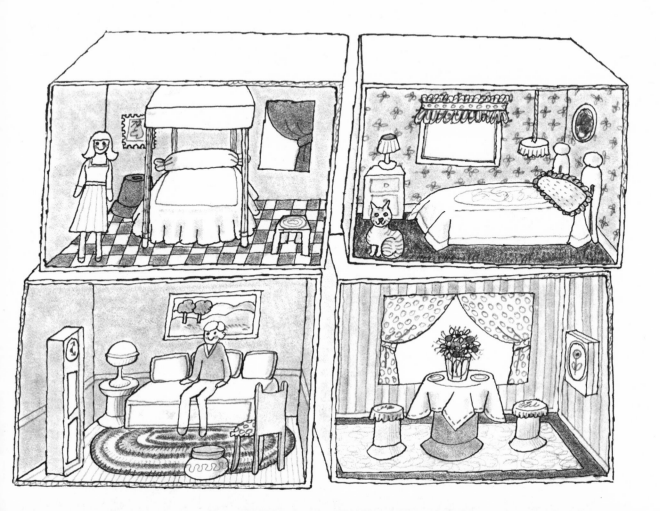

Musical Mélange

Musical instruments are easy to make and even more fun to play, especially on a rainy day.

Rhythm Sticks. Cut pieces of half-inch hardwood dowel about 10 inches long and hit them together. Or use two wooden kitchen spoons.

Wrist Bells. Sew two or three jinglebells onto a circle of elastic or onto lengths of grosgrain ribbon. Slip or tie them on wrists.

Maracas (Shakers). Put a small handful of pebbles, uncooked rice, or beans into a clear empty plastic bottle (shampoo, soda, or lotion). Make sure the cap is on tightly, and shake to your heart's content.

Chimes (Glass Harmonica). Fill glasses to different levels with water and tap lightly on the rims with a spoon. See if you can tune them to a musical scale. (Hint: the less water in the glass, the higher the note.)

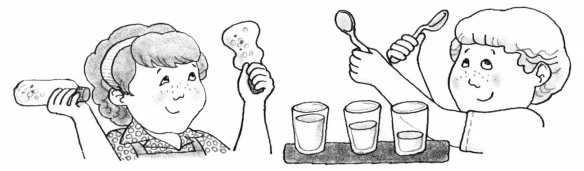

Horn. This is tricky. Blow gently across the top of an empty soda bottle. As with the chiming water glasses, add different amounts of water to a number of bottles to produce a variety of tones.

Drums. The most durable ones can be made from one-pound coffee cans, with their plastic lids. Use a wooden spoon as a drumstick. If you're more ambitious, make a Trongo: tape together 3 cans of various sizes, with lids (for example, one-pound coffee can, 2-pound coffee can, 3-pound shortening can). Make sure that the lids are at the same height. You now have a three-tone drum.

Now march away on your own, or turn on the radio or record-player and accompany it.

Otedama

Do you enjoy playing jacks? In Japan, children like to play a jacklike game with miniature beanbags. Made from fabric scraps, a set can be run up in no time at all.

You'll need:
    scraps of cotton cloth 2½ inches by 1½· inches (5 pieces for each
       set)
    needle
    thread
    rice, small beans, or sand for filling

What to do:
Fold each piece of cloth in half, with the right side on the inside, and sew up two of the three open sides, with small stitches.

Turn the little pocket right-side-out and fill it with the rice, sand, or beans.

Sew up the last side and overcast all seams for extra strength.

To play:

Version 1 (for younger kids)

Round 1: Scatter the 5 bags. Place one bag on the back of your hand. With the same hand, pick up one of the remaining bags. Flip the bag that is on the back of your hand, turn your hand over, and catch it in your palm. Repeat until all bags have been picked up.

Round 2: Scatter the bags. Place one on the back of your hand. With the same hand, pick up 2 bags. Flip the bag on the back of the hand and catch it in your palm. Put it back on the back of your hand, still holding the 2 bags, and pick up the remaining 2, then flip again, until all 5 are in your hand.

Round 3: Repeat as in Round 2, picking up first 3 and then one.

Round 4: Repeat, picking up 4 at once.

Round 5: With all 5 bags in the palm of your hand, toss them in the air and catch as many as you can on the back of your hand. Flip the remaining bags into the air and catch as many as you can.

Version 2 (for older kids)

Round 1: Scatter the 5 bags, choose one and toss it in the air. While it's in the air, pick up one of the remaining bags and catch the falling one with the same hand. Repeat until all bags are picked up.

Round 2: Scatter the bags, repeat as in Round 1, this time picking up 2 bags each time.

Round 3: Repeat as in Round 1, picking up first 3 bags and then one.

Round 4: Repeat, picking up all 4 bags.

Round 5: See Round 5, Version 1.

T-Shirt Pillow

You'll need:

    T-shirt, white or decorated

    piece of cardboard

    Magic Markers (permanent color, if possible; watercolors may run when washed)

    needle

    thread

    stuffing (polyester fiberfill, old nylon hosiery, foam rubber from old pillows)

What to do:

Slip a piece of cardboard inside the T-shirt. (This will keep the ink from bleeding through the shirt.) Decorate the shirt, front and back, with Magic Marker. (If the shirt is already decorated, skip the front.)

Remove the cardboard.

Using an overcast stitch, sew shut the neck and arm openings.

Stuff through the bottom until your "pillow" is firm.
Overcast the bottom edge. (It will look better if you turn the edges inside first.)

III. Celebrations

Parties for Birthdays and Other Days

Everyone loves parties, no matter what the occasion. Don't let the fear of high costs or lack of time for elaborate preparations stop you from celebrating. Here are some low-cost, easy ideas you can use even if the party's starting in an hour.

Paper-Strip Hats

No party's complete without hats; try this one or one made of newspapers (see Sick in Bed).

You'll need:
    lightweight cardboard strips, 1 inch wide by 24 inches long
    construction paper strips, 1 inch wide by 12 inches long
    gummed stars or seals
    feathers
    colored cellophane
    pencils
    stapler and staples
    Scotch tape or Magic Tape
    glue

What to do:
Place a cardboard strip around your head (or get someone else to) to measure it (as for a headband), remove it, and staple it together.

Cut a second cardboard strip in half and staple it to go over the top of the head (see illustration) for further support.

Take a strip of construction paper and curl it around a pencil.

Attach it to the hatband.

Use your imagination to turn strips of construction paper into chains or fringes to add onto your hat.

Decorate it with stickers, stars, feathers, etc.

Party Favors

You'll need:

    bathroom tissue tubes
    tissue paper 7 inches by 9 inches (in a pinch, use a paper towel or the Sunday funnies)
    yarn
    Scotch tape or gummed seals
    plastic sandwich bags, filled ¼ full with small candies, peanuts, balloons, or small toys

What to do:

Put each filled sandwich bag inside a paper tube.

Lay the tube along a 9-inch side of tissue paper and roll it up completely.

Secure the other 9-inch edge with tape or seals.

Tie the ends with yarn.

Marshmallow and Toothpick Construction

These sculptures make wonderful party take-homes.

You'll need:

miniature marshmallows (the colored ones are best) or gumdrops
toothpicks (the round cocktail ones are a bit more expensive but sturdier)

What to do:

Using the toothpicks speared with marshmallows as connectors, you can construct a marvelous assortment of houses, space ships, animals, and the like.

NOTE: For sturdier buildings, construct triangles first, then connect them together.

Edible Collage

Here's a double treat: an art-and-craft activity that you can eat when you're finished. Small paper cups (bathroom size, 3 oz. liquid) can be used to control the amount of sweets and other goodies each child has to work with (or eat). Each cup holds about 1 oz. of candy, nuts, raisins, or other treats.

You'll need:

paper plates, 6-inch or 9-inch (one per person)
spoons
honey
5 or 6 bathroom-size paper cups filled with:
miniature marshmallows (the colored ones are best)
pretzel sticks, corn chips, or cheese puffs

M&Ms or similar candies
gumdrops
popcorn
Cheerios (or any cereal with an interesting shape)
carrot curls or coins
raisins
peanuts or other nutmeats
flaked coconut

What to do:
Spread a spoonful of honey over the entire surface of your plate. This will form the glue for your collage.

Select several items from each cup and arrange them on your plate in a pleasing manner.

Admire the results for a while. (You could punch a hole in the top of the plate and add a string.) Then eat!

Ice Cream in a Home-made Freezer

No party is complete without ice cream. If you are feeling really daring, you might consider having each person make his or her own in home-made freezers.

Here's an easy vanilla ice cream mixture that requires no cooking and can be made ahead and chilled.

Vanilla Ice Cream

You'll need:

4 eggs
1¾ cups sugar
1½ teaspoons vanilla extract
¼ teaspoon salt
1 cup evaporated milk (8 ounces)
1 quart whole milk

What to do:

In a large bowl, beat the eggs. Add the sugar, vanilla extract, and salt, and beat again. Add milk and stir until smooth. Pour into a pitcher and refrigerate until you are ready to freeze it. This makes 2 quarts: 16 4-ounce servings.

Coffee-Can Ice Cream Freezers

Because it tends to be wet, this activity is best done outside during the summertime. If it must be done indoors, it is much easier to work on the floor. Be sure you cover the floor with plenty of newspaper and keep a mop or sponge nearby.

You'll need:

clean coffee tin with plastic lid
one-gallon plastic bucket
soup spoon
*(one of the above for each
group of 3 or 4 kids)*

5-pound bag of salt (rock salt, kosher salt, or table salt)
crushed ice (at least 2 trays for each freezer)
waterproof smocks (to protect party clothes)
ice cream mixture

What to do:

Pour 1½ cups of ice cream mixture into each coffee can. (Make sure that the can is no more than half full.)

Cover the can with its plastic lid.

Put about an inch of cracked ice in the bottom of the pail and sprinkle a spoonful of salt over it.

Place the coffee can on the ice in the pail.

Alternating layers of ice and salt, pack the bucket to within an inch of the top of the can.

Turn the can around and around in the bucket, keeping it upright.

Take turns so that nobody gets tired.

As the ice melts, replace it with layers of ice and salt.

After 10 minutes wipe off the plastic cover of the coffee can and check your mixture; it should begin to show signs of freezing.

Replace the cover, making sure that no salty water gets into the ice cream mixture, and continue turning the can until the mixture is frozen (probably another 10 minutes or so).

Now the ice cream is ready to eat.

NOTE: You can make other flavors of ice cream using this mixture as a basis. Try adding any of the following to the liquid mixture before freezing.

chocolate sauce
chocolate chips
peanuts
M&Ms
strawberries
crushed pineapple
coconut
extracts or flavorings
mashed bananas

Pitch Till You Win

No party is complete without a "loot" bag filled with raisins, nuts, balloons, and some kind of toy favor.

You can add excitement and a carnivallike atmosphere to this aspect of your party by using these as prizes in a pitch-till-you-win game. This way it also doesn't matter if all the bags aren't identical in contents.

You'll need:
 clothesline or heavy string
 clip clothespins
 marker or crayon
 2 chairs (indoors) or 2 trees (outdoors)
 "loot" bags (1 per child)
 cardboard rings (cut from tops of cornmeal or oatmeal boxes) or
   rubber jar rings used in canning

What to do:
String clothesline or string between chairs or trees.

Number the "loot" bags and clip them to the clothesline.

Give the first player a handful of rings.

Have him stand 2 or 3 feet away from the clothesline. Let him pitch the rings until he rings a clothespin and wins the prize clipped to it.

Then let the next player pitch his rings and so on until all have played and won bags.

(If the bags are too heavy for the clip pin, number both the bags and the pins. Clip just the pins to the line. As each child rings a pin, give him or her the bag with the corresponding number.)

"Today Is *Not* My Birthday!"

Celebrating someone else's special day can be very hard for young children. They need to feel loved and essential, especially when another person is getting a lot of attention. By providing enough important activities for the child to be engaged in during the festivities, you can keep jealousy to a minimum.

If a younger child is not to be included in the party or celebration, make sure what is planned for him or her to do is a pleasant, equally well planned experience, so that she doesn't feel pushed out of the way. She or he could

spend the night with a friend

have lunch at a neighbor's

go to the zoo or a puppet show with a baby-sitter.

If the child is to be present, find a special role or task, so he or she doesn't become a pest to the party child and her friends. You could

make him or her the official table setter or coat taker

let him help with passing out the prizes, setting the table, or lighting the candles.

A special helper's apron would identify him as having a special role to play.

If presents are in order, have the non-birthday child help pick out or make a present for the occasion.

A small gift could be given to the non-birthday child — something such as a new hair barrette, or a new book — either before or after the celebration, to show your appreciation of her or his help.

When You Can't Have a Party

Money short, quarantined with chicken pox, or snowed in by a blizzard? Although you may have to forgo a major celebration, here are a few suggestions to tide you over to better times.

Cake Substitutes

Not having a big cake may be disappointing, but you can still blow out the candles even if it's a single candle stuck in a doughnut or a cupcake. The feeling of being remembered will still be there.

Coupon Book

A coupon book, redeemable at a later date — or, better still, over the course of several months — will be greatly appreciated. Coupons needn't be very expensive; they can be redeemable for such items as
    an ice cream soda at a favorite place
    staying up late to see a t.v. show on a school night
    a trip to the library to pick out new books.
Coupon books can be made by kids to be given to other kids, or to adults.

In Celebration of Me

Ever watch a kid have a day when nothing seemed to be going right — plans canceled because of rain or sickness, boredom in the middle of a vacation, or simply being out of sorts?

Time for a pick-me-up that will provide something special on an otherwise dull day. Here are several ideas.

Plaster Handprint

You'll need:
- a plastic 2-cup margarine or cream cheese container or a coffee can for mixing
- a small pitcher of water
- 1 cup of plaster of paris
- a measuring cup
- a small disposable stick for stirring
- a disposable aluminum pie plate
- a paper clip

What to do:

Put ½ cup water in the can or container.

Slowly stir in the plaster.

Continue to stir until the mixture has the consistency of thick cream.

Pour it into the pie plate.

Place your outstretched hand on top of the wet plaster and hold it in position long enough to leave a firm impression.

While the plaster is still soft, insert a paper clip at one end or the other of the print (wrist edge or finger-end edge) to serve as a hanger for the finished plaque.

Write your name, age, and the date on a piece of paper and when the plaque has hardened, attach it to the back. This makes a good present for a close relative (parent, aunt or uncle, grandparent), or you can hang it in your room so you can see how fast your hand grows in a year.

NOTE: Take care when disposing of plaster. Never pour plaster down a drain.

Silhouettes

Silhouettes of famous people are often used as decorations. Here's an easy way to make silhouettes of your own important people.

You'll need:

a 12-inch by 18-inch sheet of dark construction paper for each silhouette

thumbtacks, pushpins, or masking tape (Check with an adult about which to use and which wall to use. Tape can damage wallpaper and paint, and tacks leave holes.)

a gooseneck lamp, slide projector, or other strong light source

white chalk

scissors

paste

posterboard in a bright color

What to do:

Have the person sit in a chair next to a wall, with his or her side toward the wall.

Tape or tack the construction paper to the wall at the level of the person's head.

Set up the light source and shine it straight at the paper, past the person's head, so that a shadow is cast on the paper.

Remind the person to sit very still; then trace around the shadow of the profile with a piece of chalk.

Remove the paper from the wall and very carefully cut out the silhouette.

Paste it onto a bright piece of posterboard.

A silhouette pasted onto a heart-shaped background makes a wonderful valentine.

Body Tracing

For this activity you'll need some fairly large pieces of paper. You can use a roll of butcher paper, brown wrapping paper, or you can open up and tape together several large brown grocery bags.

One person lies down on the paper, and someone else draws around him or her, making a life-size paper doll. If space permits, you might wish to strike a pose: running, jumping, hands in the air, and so on. Include as much detail in the tracing as you can — braids, fingers, and so on.

You can now decorate this life-size paper doll in several ways. Have a mirror so you can look at yourself and then draw in your facial features, hair, and clothes.

Older children might enjoy cutting out clothes from fabric, wallpaper, or construction paper to dress their dolls, including making yarn hair or dressing the doll as a character from a story or in the uniform of their favorite profession.

Or you might want to use your body tracing as a backdrop for a personal collage. Cut out pictures of your favorite things, pastimes, and so on, from magazines, and glue them on the cutout tracing.

Fished tracings can be used to decorate the walls, to remind us of our individual uniqueness.

IV. Sick in Bed

Rest and quiet are just as important as all the medicines and medical attention you get when you're trying to get better. Whether in the hospital or at home, the following activities will brighten what could otherwise be a dull stay in bed.

Before engaging in any activity that requires more than minimal movement, however, check with your doctor.

Newspaper Magic

You'll need:
a good supply of newspapers (be sure to include comics)
scissors
tape
felt-tipped pens (optional)

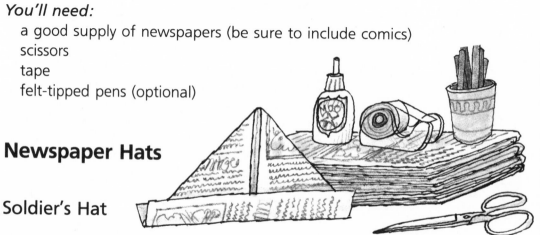

Newspaper Hats

Soldier's Hat

1. Start with a double full sheet of newspaper. Turn it horizontally, with the fold at the top.

2. Crease it vertically, down the center.

3. Fold the upper corners to the center crease, making a peak at the top.

4. Fold up the bottom of the top sheet. Turn the hat over, and fold up the remaining edge.

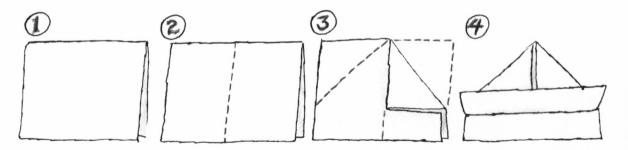

Bishop's Mitre

Follow steps 1–3 above.

4. Fold the bottom edge of the top sheet so that it just touches the triangles, then turn it up again along edges. This will make a folded band at the lower edge of hat.

5. Turn the hat over. Fold the bottom corners in to meet at the center crease.

6. Fold the lower corners up to meet the folded band.

7. Fold lower flap at folded band and tuck it into the top of the band to hold in place.

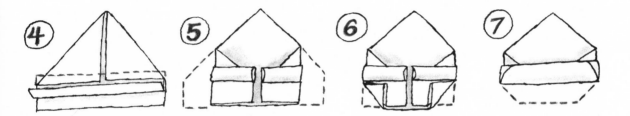

Army Hat

Follow steps for Bishop's Mitre.

8. Fold the peak of the hat down into the folded band at bottom.

Beret

Follow steps for Army Hat.

9 . Open the hat at its lower edge. The top corners will flatten out.

10 . Fold the top corners down and tuck them into the folded band at the end of the hat.

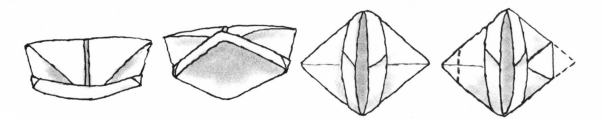

Newspaper Masks

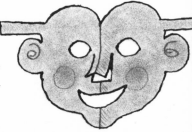

You'll need:
  a double sheet of newspaper
  scissors
  paper clips

What to do:
Cut a double fold of newspaper in half.

Fold it, as shown.

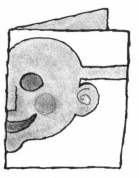

Cut features along the fold and shape the outside.

Keep it in place on your head with paper clips.

Palm Tree

You'll need:
    2 double pieces of newspaper
    tape
    scissors

What to do:
Open the two pieces of newspaper out flat as shown.

Take sheet 1 and begin rolling it into a tube.

When you reach the center of sheet 1, add in sheet 2. Continue rolling until both are rolled into a tube.

Secure the loose edges with tape.

Starting at the top of the tube, cut through all surfaces to halfway down the tube.

Make 3 or 4 additional cuts in the same direction.

Starting from the center, gently pull up on the paper. The leaves of the "tree" will begin to grow.

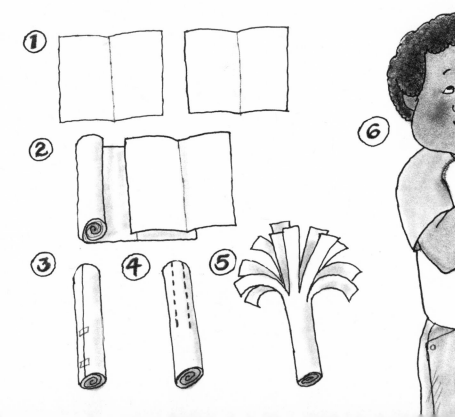

Pillowcase Pictures

You'll need:
- a piece of heavy cardboard
- an old pillowcase
- pencils
- permanent felt-tip markers

What to do:

Slip the cardboard inside the pillowcase, to provide steady backing and to prevent the colors from bleeding through.

Draw a design on the pillowcase with a pencil.

Color it in with the marking pens.

This makes a cheery addition to the convalescent's bed.

Crazy Letters

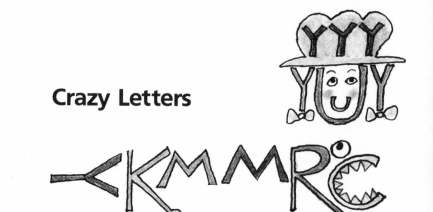

You'll need:
- paper
- pens
- crayons

What to do:

Print some capital letters on a clean sheet of paper and see what pictures you can turn them into.

Yarn Babies

You'll need:
    light cardboard
    scissors
    yarn
    yarn needle (thick, blunt needle with a big eye)
    embroidery or crewel thread
    embroidery or crewel needle

What to do:
Cut a piece of cardboard twice the length of the doll's arm, plus the width of the body.

Wind yarn around it about 12 times in the long direction, then slide the yarn off carefully. Using either yarn or embroidery thread, tie off each end about ¾ of an inch in. These two ends will become the hands.

Cut another piece of cardboard the height you want your doll. Wind yarn around it the long way about 24 times. Slide off this loop as you did for the arms.

Tie the longer, bigger piece in two places: about ½ inch from the end and another ¾ inch farther down. (These will be for hair and head.)

Slip the arm and hand yarn through the body yarn right below to the place you've tied for the head. Tie the body piece again just under these arms.

Cut the top loops for hair.

Embroider on a face with embroidery thread.

For a doll wearing a dress, leave as she is. For a doll wearing pants, tie another piece of yarn or thread about an inch below the under-arms tie, then divide the bottom part of the yarn doll and tie two ankles (like the hands, above).

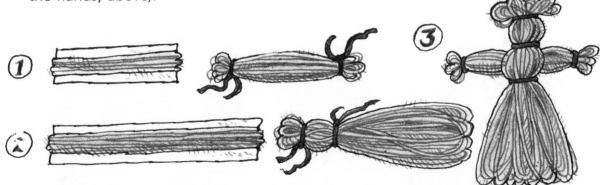

Shadow Pictures

You'll need:
 a clear wall
 a table lamp on the other side of you

What to do:
With your hands between the light source and the wall, try casting shadows that look like animals.

Shadow Puppets

You'll need:
 paper
 animal cookie cutters
 a paper punch
 scissors
 tape
 drinking straws or popsicle sticks
 a flashlight or table lamp

What to do:
Using the cookie cutters as patterns, trace and cut out animals.

Punch eyes where needed, using the paper punch.

Tape the animal shapes to popsicle sticks or straws.

Shine the flashlight on the puppets so that they cast shadows on the wall. Make up stories and act them out with your puppets.

You can also make a shadow box for your puppets.

Get a medium-sized cardboard carton. Cut the flaps off the top; cut out the bottom to look like a t.v. set.

Tape a piece of tracing paper across the inside of the opening to make a screen.

Shine a bright light from behind the box.

Use the shadow puppets or make others.

You can make puppets to go with your favorite story record and use the record as a soundtrack for your show.

Paper Beads

You'll need:
    template for a small triangle (can be made of cardboard)
    newspaper, wallpaper, or colored construction paper
    a knitting needle or a thin drinking straw
    scissors
    glue
    a yarn needle
    yarn or light string

What to do:
Trace the template onto the paper and cut out a triangle.

Starting at a wide edge, roll the paper around the knitting needle or straw.

Place a drop of glue at the tip to prevent the bead from unrolling.

Make more beads.

String them.

Wiggle Worms

You'll need:

   pencils
   glue
   colored pipe cleaners (the 12-inch chenille ones are best)
   scissors
   magnetic tape (available in rolls in most hardware stores)
   teeny wiggle eyes
   a horseshoe magnet
   a piece of lightweight cardboard or a paper plate

What to do:

Wrap pipe cleaner around each of several pencils, forming a tight coil. If the ends are sharp, turn them under slightly.

Glue a pair of wiggle eyes to one end of each.

Cut a ⅜-inch piece of magnetic tape and secure it to the underside of the worm.

Place the worms on the cardboard, and, holding the magnet underneath it, make the worms scurry around by moving the magnet.

You could draw a maze on the cardboard and see if the worms can find their way through it.

When you have finished racing your worms, they can be used for holding up memos on your refrigerator door.

One-Armed Activities

Arm in a cast or attached to an IV? These ideas will surely amuse a "one-armed bandit."

Ring-Toss Box

You'll need:
a sturdy cardboard box with a lid (approximately 7 by 10 by 2 inches)
scissors (for punching holes)
10 wooden clothespins
marker
3 to 5 canning jar rubbers

What to do:
Punch two rows of 5 evenly spaced holes each in the box lid.

Insert the clothespins in the holes.

Number them from 1 to 10.

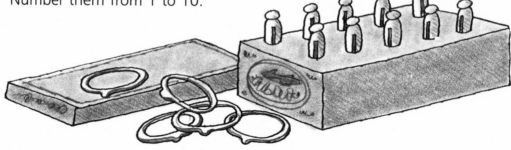

Place the box at the foot of the bed. The patient should be in a sitting position.

Toss the rings over the clothespins and add up the score.

The first player to reach 25 or any other number you choose will be the winner.

NOTE: When you are finished, store the clothespins and jar rubbers inside the box.

Bedside Beanbags

You'll need:

a rolled-up small paper bag or two, or a regular beanbag
string
a clean empty wastebasket or several shoeboxes

What to do:

Securely attach to the bean bag or paper bags a string 4 to 6 feet long. Tie the other end to your waist.

Set up the target (the wastebasket) within reach of the string.

You will be able to aim at the target and retrieve your own beanbag.

Color Trays

You'll need:

white plastic ice-cube trays (mini-cube or regular) or a white Styrofoam egg carton
an eye-dropper
red, yellow, and blue "mock food color" (see page 19)
warm water

What to do:

Fill the tray or egg carton half-full with lukewarm water.

Add a bit of red to one cup, yellow to another, blue to a third.

Using the dropper, see how many different colors you can make by mixing them in the remaining cups on the tray.

Or use the colors to "paint" pictures on white paper towels.

NOTE: If this activity is to be done in bed, protect the bedding with waterproof covering (an old plastic tablecloth or a large plastic garbage bag) and use a lap tray to provide a firm base for the color trays.

Finger or Toe Puppets

You'll need:

felt or scraps of fake fur
glue
scissors
odds and ends for decoration

What to do:

Using the pattern given here, cut two pieces of felt or fur fabric.

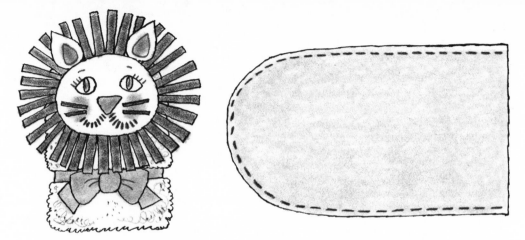

Put glue along the dotted line on the back side of one piece of the fur (on either side of the felt).

Lay the other piece of fur or felt on top and press both together.

Let it set for about 5 minutes.

Decorate it.

Variations:
Cut the fingers off an old pair of gloves and decorate them.

Using a fine-line marker, give your finger puppets faces. Use toothpaste caps for hats.

NOTE: Finger puppets make good covers for finger casts. Placed on the toes of someone with a foot cast, they'll encourage him or her to wiggle and exercise the toes.

V. On the Road

Visiting

Going "prepared" is the best way to visit adult friends or relatives who rarely entertain children. For younger children a small blanket or beach towel, spread down in a corner, will help to define the boundaries of the play area. The size of the lunchbox kit or small knapsack (see below, page 65) can help to limit the choices of things that can be brought along. Be sure to keep in mind where you're going and whether the things you're bringing along are appropriate. In general, leave potentially messy activities — paints, play dough — at home. Your hosts won't appreciate a stain on a rug or wallpaper to remind them of your stay!

Things to take visiting:
  puzzles
  pencil game books
  several pencils with erasers
  story books
  a cassette recorder with story cassettes
  small dolls
  Matchbox cars
  dominoes
  checkers and a board
  computer games (the self-contained kind)
  small sets of building materials:
    Tinker Toys
    blocks
    Legos
    Bristle Blocks

Lunchbox Traveling Kit

A metal lunchbox, the rectangular school kind, makes a useful traveling companion. Its compact size makes it easy for even a two-year-old to carry.

You'll need:

a new or used metal lunchbox with a good clasp
blackboard paint
contact paper
nontoxic spray enamel

The box can be painted inside and out with nontoxic spray enamel or covered with contact paper. (Paint may not cover rusty spots on a used box.) Paint the lid with blackboard paint (available by the quart from most big hardware stores) to provide additional writing space. Now you're ready to pack it with a variety of things. Remember to keep in mind where you are going as you choose them. If you're going visiting, check the list on page 64 for suitable things to take. Drawing materials, glue, scissors, and snacks may require supervision.

Here are some things that will travel well.

For younger kids (ages 2 to 5):
chalk
small sponge for an eraser
magnetic letters (they'll stick to the lid)
spiral notepad
crayons
quarter-size sheets of construction paper
scissors
glue stick
1 or 2 finger puppets
deck of miniature playing cards for kids
gummed labels or stickers
colored pencils
1 or 2 small story books
a box of raisins or animal crackers and a small can of juice for a snack
a small bottle of bubble-blowing solution (for outdoor use)
straws for blowers (for outdoor use)

For older kids (ages 6 to 8):

chalk

small sponge for an eraser

Wiggle Worms and magnet for racing them (see Sick in Bed section)

a small Fun Pad or other pocket-sized game books

a pocket checker game

a pack of playing cards

other card games

colored pencils

notebook

6 clothespins and canning-jar rubbers, to turn the box into a ring-toss game (fasten the clothespins to the edges of the box)

pocket-sized jigsaw puzzle

books

individual packages of raisins, pretzels, or other snacks

bubble-blowing solution (for outdoor use)

straws for blowing bubbles (for outdoor use)

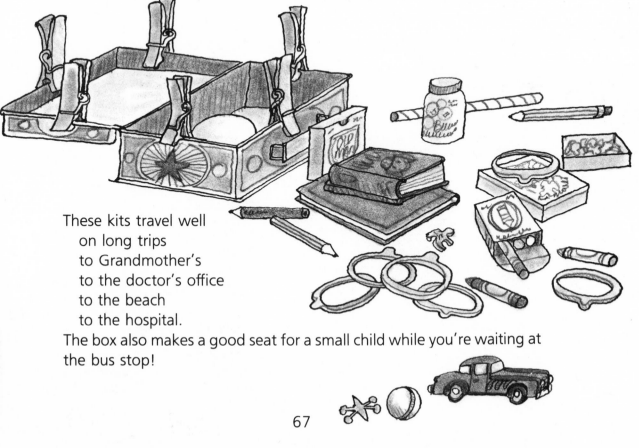

These kits travel well
 on long trips
 to Grandmother's
 to the doctor's office
 to the beach
 to the hospital.

The box also makes a good seat for a small child while you're waiting at the bus stop!

Older kids (9-plus) may enjoy:

Traveler's All-in-One Fun Pad/Trip Diary

You'll need:
    an 8 by 10 spiral notebook
    puzzles and games cut from newspapers and magazines
    glue
    scissors
    2 brown clasp envelopes, 5 by 8 size

What to do:
Glue the envelopes inside the front and back covers of the notebook.

They can be used later to hold pencils, pens, postcards, maps, and guide books.

Divide the notebook in half. Use the pages in the front half for games, puzzles, doodling, and so on. The second half will be used for your trip diary.

Glue your collection of games and puzzles clipped from newspapers and magazines onto the pages at the front.

Label the next pages in the front section with the names of games you might want to play: Hangman, Capture the Square, Tic-Tac-Toe, Word Search, and so on. Leave some pages free for doodling.

In the second half of your notebook, allow 2 to 3 pages per day of your trip, and label each section accordingly. Doing this will allow you enough space to record your daily activities as well as to glue in a postcard of or leaflet about a place you visited.

You might want to leave a few pages at the back for autographs or the addresses of new friends you meet along the way.

When your trip is over, you'll have a wonderful record of your experience.

Waiting

In Line

Armed with a wristwatch (with a second hand), memo pad, and pencil, you can turn waiting in line into an observation experience. Here are some things to try.

How fast does the line move? Record the time when you get into the line. How long will it take you to reach the front of the line? Record each person's guess and see whose comes closest.

After 1 minute, count how many people have joined the line behind you. How long is the line after 5 minutes? 10?

Are you on a street with traffic passing? Count how many cars pass by in 1, 3, or 5 minutes.

Record all out-of-state license plates.

What if the theater runs out of tickets before your group or family gets to the booth? Enlist everyone's help to make a list of alternatives: possible activities that could be substituted if necessary.

Pocket pals to bring along to help pass the time while waiting in line:

a yo-yo
a yard of string for a cat's cradle
a small magnifying glass
a miniature joke book or riddle book

In a Restaurant

Close your eyes and listen for a few minutes to all the sounds around you. Try to write down as many different ones as you can.

Write the name of the restaurant at the top of a piece of paper. How many other words can you find in the name before the waiter brings your order?

Still waiting? Try a cumulative story. One person starts telling a story and stops at any given point. The next person continues. The story can go on until it's finished or your dinner is served — whichever comes first!

Games for Restaurants and Waiting Rooms

What's Missing. Search your pockets or purse for several easily identifiable objects. Place from 3 to 6 things on the table and let someone study them for a few minutes. Have him close his eyes while you remove one of the items. When he opens his eyes, have him guess what is missing. Now it's your turn.

I Spy. Look around the waiting room and select an object. Describe it to someone else. Give one clue at a time until she guesses what it is. Then it's her turn to give clues to you.

Magic Magnifier. Use a small magnifying glass to examine things: a stamp, a penny, a piece of yarn, a safety pin, for example. Other things to look at: your fingertips, skin, words in a book. You'll be amazed at how much entertainment you can derive from doing this.

Quiet Places

Church services, lectures, concerts, and some waiting areas place demands on us all for a certain amount of quiet. A few inconspicuous activities will tide you over an especially long session.

A picture book, especially if somehow related to the environment you are in (for example, Bible story book), is probably one of your best choices.

Notebooks and pencils are good standbys for games of Tic-Tac-Toe or Hangman or for taking notes.

For coin rubbings, take 3 or 4 coins and put them under a sheet of paper, with something stiff, such as a book, under them. Rub a soft lead pencil back and forth so that the pattern on the coin appears. Later you could glue this sheet to thin cardboard, cut out the coins, and use them for play money.

Handkerchief Tricks

What could be quieter than a handkerchief? Keep an extra one handy for these tricks.

Hankie Baby

Lay a handkerchief out flat.

Roll both sides toward the middle.

Fold the top half (A) down about two-thirds of the way over the bottom half (B).

Pull the B half up between the lower two rolled edges.

Unroll the ends of the rolls slightly and pull them gently to either side. Bring the B edges back to tie off C as a head, and to form the arms of the doll.

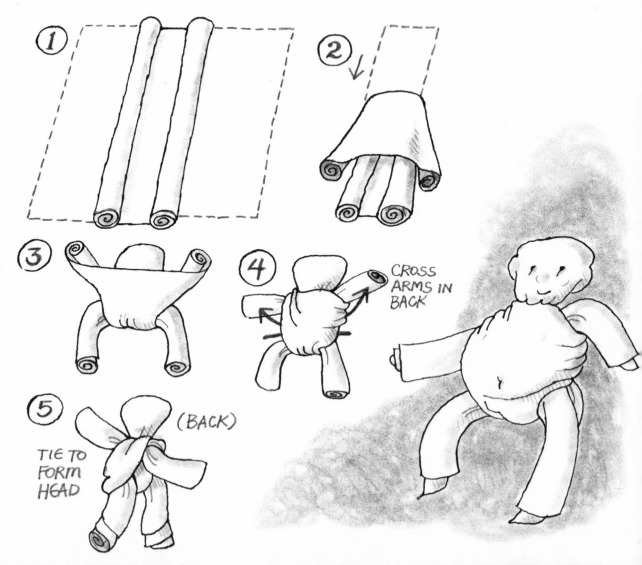

①

② ↓

③

④ CROSS ARMS IN BACK

⑤ (BACK)

TIE TO FORM HEAD

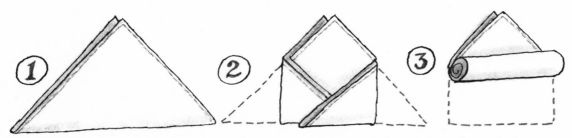

Firecracker

Fold handkerchief to form a triangle.

Turn in the two bottom points, letting one overlap the other slightly, so that the handkerchief looks like an open envelope.

Starting at the bottom, roll up the handkerchief until only a small triangle remains.

Pick up the handkerchief by the sides, rolled side facing away from you and the end of the triangle hanging down.

Fold the rolled ends toward you, overlapping one over the other slightly.

Holding the overlapped ends in your left hand (or your right if you are lefthanded), take the points and fold them over the overlapped ends, tucking them into the center of the roll.

Stuff the ends farther into the center, while unrolling the other side around them. Keep stuffing and unrolling until the ends appear (you may need to untuck the tips).

To "pop" the firecracker, just pull the tips.

Handkerchief Mouse

To make a handkerchief mouse, don't pop the firecracker. Instead, take one end and spread it sideways, twisting the ends until they are rolled tightly. Tie the ends in a knot to form ears and the head.

Off to the Market

Do you hate to go shopping with your folks because your kid brother is always pestering them to buy stuff that's not on the list, or you think it's just too boring? Here are a couple of ideas that will make your parents happy, keep your brother occupied, and might even earn you a few extra cents.

Supermarket Lotto

Make a set of picture shopping cards for a young child to use while shopping. Cut pictures of easy-to-recognize products from the colorful circulars in the Sunday newspaper or from empty boxes or cartons (butter, eggs, crackers) and paste them onto 3 by 5 notecards or squares of cardboard. Pass them out to the child one at a time, and have him search for each item and put it into the basket when he finds it.

Coupon Clipper

If your mother doesn't save coupons, perhaps you can earn a few extra cents by becoming the family "super coupon clipper." Most large newspapers have a certain day of the week, like Wednesday, when there will be a lot of coupons. Check the paper for coupons for items your family uses often. Before you go shopping, check your shopping list against the coupons in your file. At the store, hand the coupons to the cashier before she rings up the purchases. Perhaps you can work out a deal with your family and either get to keep the cents saved by the use of the coupons, or offer to split the difference — it will impress your family that you're becoming a good junior consumer.

VI. Exploring the Great Out-of-Doors

Field trips don't have to take you miles away from home. When was the last time you took a good look at what's growing in the cracks of the sidewalk, adopted a neighborhood tree, or really watched the clouds? Whether you're surrounded by concrete, blacktop, or a rolling meadow, there are a myriad of wonderful things to do and explore right outside your door.

Around Home and School

Scavenger Hunt

A scavenger hunt can offer the opportunity to take a closer look at things we "see" every day.

You'll need:
    a bag for collecting specimens
    a magnifying glass
    paper
    pencils
    crayons (to draw pictures of things you don't want to take from their
        natural environments)
    small plastic bags
    a notebook or a pad of paper

What to do:

Go outside, close your eyes, and listen for a moment. Open them and list at least 3 different sounds you heard.

Are there plants or trees nearby? How many different kinds of leaves can you see?

Find the leaf whose shape you like best. Why is it your favorite?

Find something from a plant other than a leaf.

Find something that you think doesn't belong outside.

Make 3 ''mystery rubbings'' and think of 2 clues apiece to help people guess what they are.

To make a mystery rubbing, place a sheet of paper over a nearly flat object (such as a leaf) and rub the paper gently with a soft pencil or crayon until the outline of the object becomes visible.

Choose one side of a building (or house). How many windows can you see?

Look at the building and list up to 6 different materials that were used in making it. Describe the ways they look and feel (if you can touch them).

Find something that is living and something that is dead.

Find a good place to hide.

On the Pavement

You'll need:
chalk
measuring tape
ruler
string
pencils
a pad of paper or a spiral notebook for each person

What to do:

Line games with chalk (for groups): How long is the line that we as a group make if we stand shoulder-to-shoulder? If we stand in a line, one in back of another? If we stand side-by-side with our arms outstretched and our fingertips touching? If we stand with our legs spread apart and our arms spread out with our fingers touching? How could we measure the actual length of these lines? With our feet? Using standard or metric measurement? With string?

How big is the biggest circle we could make with our bodies? How little is the smallest circle we could make? How many ways could we measure and draw these circles?

How many different kinds of weed can you find growing in the cracks of the pavement? How many ways can you classify them? Why do you think they are growing through the pavement?

Tracing body parts: Trace everybody's hands in chalk on the blacktop. How many are there? How can you arrange them? How many fingers are there altogether? How many thumbs? Can you make a picture with your hands as you trace them? How long would a line of all your hands be? Can you arrange your hands from the smallest to the largest, and trace them in a line? Are the people with the smallest hands the smallest people? Try tracing everybody's feet. Does any of you have a foot that is just a foot long? How many feet long are all your feet together? How long are all your right feet together? Does everybody have two feet the same length? Who has a pair of feet with the greatest difference in size?

Body shapes: What sorts of shapes can you outline on the blacktop using two bodies? Can you incorporate their shadows into the drawings? Can you create a monster outline by tracing the bodies of two or more people? How many arms and legs does it have? Make up a story about your monster or about anything else you have drawn using people's bodies.

What other activities could you create using these ideas?

Adopt a Tree

You'll need:
  a tree
  black marking crayons
  ½ yard of muslin
  a magnifying glass
  notebooks
  pencils

What to do:

Adopt a tree that you pass frequently — outside your door, on your way to the park or the store or school.

Make bark rubbings. Have two people hold the muslin tight against the tree, while a third makes a rubbing, using a large black marking crayon.

Visit your tree several times during the year at different seasons; notice its seasonal changes.

Try different ways of measuring your tree. How many people does it take to surround it? How long a piece of string is needed to go around it? Measure your tree again later in the year. Did it grow? What lives in your tree? How do you know? Make a list of all the different birds, ants, insects, and so on, you find near your tree.

Take pictures of your group and their tree.

Shadow Games and Tricks

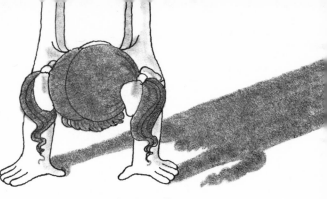

You'll need:
 kids
 a sunny day

What to do:
What is the biggest shadow you can cast with your body? The smallest?
The longest? The shortest?

Does your shadow move when you move?

Try hiding your shadow.

Can you jump on your shadow?

With a friend or two, try making a shadow with two heads, three legs,
and five arms.

Can you make your shadows appear as if each person is standing on
another's arms?

Try to get away from your shadow.

Can you shake hands with your shadow?

Use different objects to cast shadows.

Motel for Minibeasts

On a romp through the woods, in the park, or even in your own backyard, young insect enthusiasts are bound to return laden with spiders, grasshoppers, ladybugs, and the like. Think of these as only temporary visitors, allowing them to go free after you've had a chance to watch them for a while.

Wide-mouth jars of any size make good bug houses. Just punch a few holes in the lid for air. Be sure to add a bit of grass and a twig for your insect to climb on.

Cut a square hole in the side of a quart or half-gallon milk carton. Tape a piece of nylon net or plastic screening over the hole to make a window for viewing your insects. Put the insects in from top. Use a paper clip to secure the top edges and to keep the bugs inside until it's time to free them.

Long boxes such as the ones spaghetti and lasagna come in, with cellophane windows, can serve as temporary shelters for grasshoppers or caterpillars.

Ants are great fun to watch, and you'll want to make a more permanent home where you can observe them for several days or weeks. Put several inches of dirt or sand in a one-gallon jar. Make sure it has a good lid with a few holes punched in it. Add enough water to dampen the soil, then put in your ants and some food. Be careful not to put in too much food: just a few crumbs or a tiny piece of hamburger. Add a piece of of absorbent cotton and keep it damp by adding a few drops of water to it each day. Now you can watch your ants live and work.

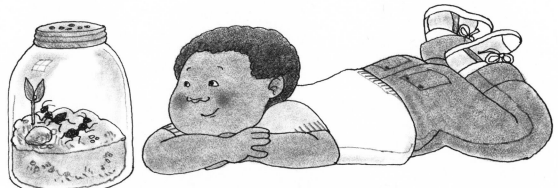

Down by the Sea

At the beach, sand, shells, and water are yours for the taking. Here are a few ideas to get you started.

Sand Equipment

Sand Pail. A one-gallon plastic pail is much more durable than the sand pails usually available commercially.

Spade or Shovel. Try to get one with a good handle made of wood or metal; the plastic ones usually bend or crack fairly easily. Large clamshells will make excellent spades; look for them.

Sand Combs. Cut corrugated cardboard into a variety of comb shapes to leave pleasant patterns in damp sand.

Sifters. With masking tape, attach a piece of Fiberglas screening to one end of a tunafish can from which both ends have been removed. (Be sure that the can has no rough edges.)

For a Super Sand Set. Gather from your kitchen a large plastic colander, a ladle, long-handled wooden spoons, funnels, measuring cups, cookie cutters, and old aluminum salt and pepper or flour shakers. Store them all in a net shopping bag.

NOTE: Discount department stores often have "dollar sales" several times a year where you can pick up plastic housewares rather cheaply. These are great to use for sand and water play.

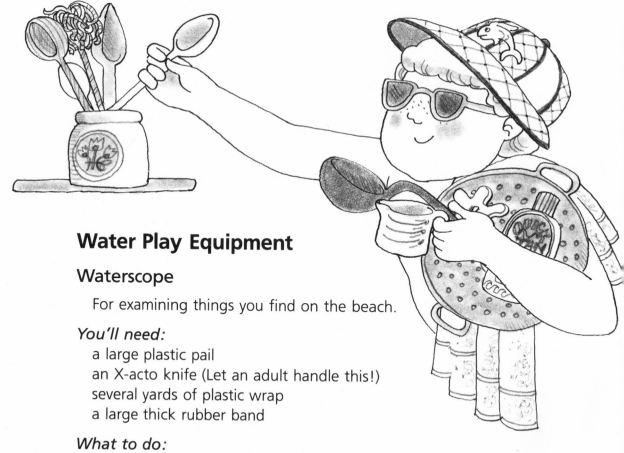

Water Play Equipment

Waterscope

For examining things you find on the beach.

You'll need:
a large plastic pail
an X-acto knife (Let an adult handle this!)
several yards of plastic wrap
a large thick rubber band

What to do:
Have an adult cut 2 or 3 holes with the knife in the sides of the pail.

Stretch the plastic wrap loosely across the top; fasten it with the rubber band.

Fill the top cavity with water.

Hold inside the pail under the plastic wrap any object you want to study.

Water Lens

For looking under the water.

You'll need:
the same materials as for the Waterscope

What to do:
Cut the bottom out of the pail.

Stretch the plastic wrap loosely over the top of the pail; fasten it securely with the rubber band.

Place the end with the plastic wrap into the water.

Look through the cut-off bottom end; you should be able to see what's going on under the water!

For a super water play set, collect:
   a small plastic basin
   about 3 feet of clear plastic hose
   corks
   a bulb kitchen baster
   plastic containers
   sponges
You can store everything in the basin.

Shore Collections

Styrofoam egg cartons make good homes for small objects found along the shore. See how many different kinds of shells, pebbles, beach glass (only the smooth kind), and seaweed you can find. As your collection grows, you can expand into new egg cartons.

Sand Casting

You'll need:
   sand
   a bucket
   water
   plaster of paris
   a found object (shell, beach glass, etc.)

What to do:

Prepare the sand mold for your cast by digging a shallow hole in the sand and smoothing it out. You can make it whatever shape you like.

Decorate the mold with your found objects, or make an imprint with a stick or by pressing your hand in. If you want to write words, make sure you write them backward, because the mold will create a mirror image.

Following the directions on the package, mix the plaster in your bucket; pour it into the mold.

Let it dry for 15 to 20 minutes before removing it from the sand.

Brush off any loose sand. Your plaster cast is done.

You can paint your cast afterward or glue more things onto it.